Dad played his trumpet.

He played in the house.

Floppy barked at Dad.

Dad played in the garage.

Floppy barked at Dad.

Dad played in the shed.

Floppy barked at Dad.

Dad played in a band.

The band played in the park.

Floppy went to the park.

The band played.

Floppy barked.

Floppy barked and barked.

The band couldn't play.

"What a bad dog!" said Dad.